Dash Diet Cookbook

Quick and Easy Guide with Recipes for Weight Loss and Lower Your Blood Pressure.
Cut Cholesterol with Healthy Recipes.
Regain Confidence with Mediterranean Lifestyle to Prevent Hypertension.

America Daily Cooking

Table of Contents

Introduction

The DASH diet leans heavily on vegetables, fruits, and whole grains. Fish and lean poultry are served moderately. Whole wheat flour is used instead of white flour. DASH as a diet plan promotes the consumption of low-fat dairy, lean meat, fruits, and vegetables. It is literally a mix of old world and new world eating plans. It has been designed to follow old world diet principles to help eliminate new world health problems.

The carbohydrates are mainly made of plant fiber which the body does not easily digest and therefore cannot turn into stored fat. The plan is rich in good fats that make food taste good and help us feel fuller for a longer period of time. Proteins are not forbidden but are geared more toward plant-based protein and not so much meat consumption.

When filling the plate for a meal, it is important that the food be attractive as well as tasty and nutritious. A wide variety of foods will make this plan much more interesting. Try to make choices that will offer a range of colors and textures. And remember that dessert is not off limits but should be based around healthy choices that include fresh fruit.

The DASH eating plans emphasis on vegetables, fruits, whole grains, and low-fat dairy products makes it an ideal plan for anyone looking to gain health through lowered blood pressure and a healthier heart. It is a heart healthy way of eating. The DASH plan has no specialized recipes or food plans. Daily caloric intake depends on a person's activity level and age. People who need to lose weight would naturally eat fewer calories.

The DASH diet's major focus is on grains, vegetables, and fruits because these foods are higher fiber foods and will make you feel full longer. Whole grains should be consumed six to eight times daily, vegetables four to six servings daily, and fruit four to five servings daily. Low-fat dairy is an important part of the diet and should be eaten two to three times daily. And there should be six or fewer servings daily of fish, poultry, and lean meat.

The DASH diet focuses on long-term healthy eating habits. The diet doesn't force you to starve or battle constant cravings. Instead, it focuses on understanding food groups, controlling portion sizes, and making sure you get the optimal levels of potassium, calcium, magnesium, fiber, and protein.

The diet focuses certain food groups for specific reasons: Fruits and vegetables give you the magnesium and potassium your body needs, and low-fat dairy products provide calcium. Every food you eat should have a purpose, and that's the most important principle of the DASH diet: eat well so you feel well. Here are some additional points to remember when you're following the DASH principles:

Reduce your sodium intake. The diet recommends less than 2,300 mg of sodium per day. The National Heart, Lung and Blood Institute recommends lowering the sodium intake even further—to 1,500 mg—for people with high blood pressure, people with diabetes or chronic kidney disease, African Americans, and people aged 51 and over.

Eat fruits, vegetables, and low-fat dairy products

Focus on high-fiber foods

Eat more healthy fats, which are good for your heart, instead of saturated fats

Achieve and maintain a healthy body weight

Eat a lot of potassium and magnesium

Stay hydrated by drinking plenty of plain water

Avoid smoking

The DASH diet is more than just a diet—it's a lifestyle.

Dressings, Sauces & Seasoning

Cranberry Sauce

Servings: 6

Preparation time: 10 minutes

Cooking Time: 15 minutes

Ingredients

- 12 ounces fresh cranberries
- 1 cup powdered Erythritol
- ¾ cup water
- 1 teaspoon fresh lemon zest, grated
- ½ teaspoon organic vanilla extract

Directions:

1. Place the cranberries, water, and Erythritol and lemon zest in a medium pan and mix well.

2. Place the pan over medium heat and bring to a boil.

3. Adjust the heat to low and simmer for about 12-15 minutes, stirring frequently.

4. Remove the pan from heat and mix in the vanilla extract.

5. Set aside at room temperature to cool completely.

6. Transfer the sauce into a bowl and refrigerate to chill before serving.

Nutrition:

Calories: 32

Net Carbs: 3.1g

Carbohydrate: 5.2g

Fiber: 2.1g

Protein: 0g

Fat: 0g

Sugar: 2.1g

Sodium: 160mg

Ketchup

Servings: 12

Preparation time: 10 minutes

Cooking Time: 30 minutes

Ingredients

- 6 ounces sugar-free tomato paste
- 1 cup water
- ¼ cup powdered Erythritol
- 3 tablespoons balsamic vinegar
- ½ teaspoon garlic powder
- ½ teaspoon onion powder
- ¼ teaspoon paprika
- 1/8 teaspoon ground cloves
- 1/8 tsp mustard powder
- Salt, as required

Directions:

1. Add all the ingredients in a small pan and beat until smooth.

2. Now, place the pan over medium heat and bring to a gentle simmer, stirring continuously.

3. Adjust the heat to low and simmer, covered for about 30 minutes or until desired thickness, stirring occasionally.

4. Remove the pan from heat and let it cool completely before serving.

5. You can preserve this ketchup in the refrigerator by placing in an airtight container.

Nutrition:

Calories: 13

Net Carbs: 2.3g

Carbohydrate: 2.9g

Fiber: 0.6g

Protein: 0.7g

Fat: 0.1g

Sugar: 1.8g

Sodium: 26mg

Note: For the best consistency, puree the ketchup in a high-speed blender until smooth.

Cilantro Sauce

Servings: 6

Preparation time: 10 minutes

Cooking time: 5 minutes

Ingredients

- ½ cup plain Greek yogurt
- ½ cup fresh cilantro, chopped
- 6 garlic cloves, peeled
- 1 jalapeño pepper, chopped

- Salt, as required
- ¼ cup water

Directions:

1. Add all the ingredients in a blender and pulse until smooth.

2. Transfer the sauce into a bowl and set aside for about 15-20 minutes before serving.

Nutrition:

Calories: 20

Net Carbs: 2.4g

Carbohydrate: 2.6g

Fiber: 0.2g

Protein: 1.4g

Fat: 0.3g

Sugar: 1.6g

Sodium: 43mg

Avocado Sauce

Servings: 8

Preparation time: 15 minutes

Cooking time: 0 minutes

Ingredients

1. 2 avocados, peeled, pitted and chopped

2. ½ cup yellow onion, chopped

3. 1 cup fresh cilantro leaves

4. 2 garlic cloves, chopped

5. 1 jalapeño pepper, chopped
6. 1 cup homemade vegetable broth

7. 2 tablespoons fresh lemon juice

8. 2 teaspoons balsamic vinegar

9. 1 teaspoon ground cumin

10. Pinch of cayenne pepper

11. Salt, as required

Directions:

1. Add all the ingredients in a blender and pulse until smooth.

2. Serve immediately.

Nutrition:

Calories: 115

Net Carbs: 2.1g

Carbohydrate: 5.8g

Fiber: 3.7g

Protein: 1.8g

Fat: 10.1g

Sugar: 0.8g

Sodium: 120mg

Herbed Capers Sauce

Servings: 4

Preparation time: 10 minutes

Cooking time: 0 minutes

Ingredients

- ½ cup fresh parsley, finely chopped
- 3 tablespoons fresh basil, finely chopped
- 2 garlic cloves, crushed
- 1 tablespoon fresh lemon juice
- 2 tablespoons small capers
- ¾ cup olive oil
- Salt and ground black pepper, as required

Directions:

1.   Add all the ingredients into a shallow bowl and with an immersion blender, blend until the desired consistency is achieved.

2. Serve immediately.

Nutrition:

Calories: 331

Net Carbs: 0.8g

Carbohydrate: 1.3g

Fiber: 0.5g

Protein: 0.5g

Fat: 38g

Sugar: 0.2g

Sodium: 172mg

Basil Pesto

Servings: 6

Preparation time: 10 minutes

Cooking time: 0 minutes

Ingredients

- 2 cups fresh basil
- 4 garlic cloves, peeled
- 2/3 cup Parmesan cheese, grated
- 1/3 cup pine nuts
- ½ cup olive oil
- Salt and ground black pepper, as required

Directions:

1. Place the basil, garlic, Parmesan cheese and pine nuts in a food processor and pulse until a chunky mixture is formed.

2. While the motor is running gradually, add the oil and pulse until smooth.

3. Now, add the salt, and black pepper and pulse until well combined.

4. Serve immediately.

Nutrition:

Calories: 232

Net Carbs: 1.4g

Carbohydrate: 1.9g

Fiber: 0.5g

Protein: 5g

Fat: 24.2g

Sugar: 0.3g

Sodium: 104mg

Veggie Hummus

Servings: 8

Preparation time: 10 minutes

Cooking time: 0 minutes

Ingredients

- 2½ tablespoons olive oil, divided
- 1 cup zucchini, peeled and chopped
- ¾ cup pumpkin puree
- ¼ cup tahini
- 2 tablespoons fresh lemon juice
- 1 teaspoon ground cumin
- 1 teaspoon garlic powder
- ½ teaspoon smoked paprika
- Salt, as required

Directions:

1. Place 2 tablespoons of oil and the remaining ingredients in a blender and pulse until smooth.

2. Place the hummus into a bowl and drizzle with remaining oil.

3. Serve immediately.

Nutrition:

Calories: 96

Net Carbs: 2.7g

Carbohydrate: 4.4g

Fiber: 1.7g

Protein: 1.9g

Fat: 8.6g

Sugar: 1.2g

Sodium: 32mg

Tzatziki

Servings: 12

Preparation time: 10 minutes

Cooking time: 0 minutes

Ingredients

- 1 large English cucumber, peeled and grated
- Salt, as required
- 2 cups plain Greek yogurt
- 1 tablespoon fresh lemon juice
- 4 garlic cloves, minced
- 1 tablespoon fresh mint leaves, chopped
- 2 tablespoons fresh dill, chopped

- Pinch of cayenne pepper
- Freshly ground black pepper, as required

Directions:

1. Arrange a colander in the sink.

2. Place the cucumber into colander and sprinkle with salt.

3. Let it drain for about 10-15 minutes.

4. With your hands, squeeze the cucumber well.

5. Place the cucumber and remaining ingredients in a large bowl and stir to combine.

6. Cover the bowl and refrigerate to chill for at least 4-8 hours before serving.

Nutrition:

Calories: 36

Net Carbs: 4.2g

Carbohydrate: 4.5g

Fiber: 0.3g

Protein: 2.7g

Fat: 0.6g

Sugar: 3.3g

Sodium: 42mg

Baba Ghanoush

Servings: 8

Preparation time: 15 minutes

Cooking Time: 35 minutes

Ingredients

- 2 large eggplants
- 3 teaspoons olive oil
- 2 garlic cloves, chopped
- 2 tablespoons tahini
- 2 tablespoons fresh lemon juice
- 1 teaspoon ground cumin
- Salt and ground black pepper, as required
- 1 tablespoon fresh parsley leaves

Directions:

1. Preheat the oven to 400 degrees F. Grease a baking dish.

2. Arrange the eggplants into prepared baking dish in a single layer.

3. Bake for about 35 minutes.

4. Remove the eggplants from oven and immediately, place into a bowl of cold water to cool slightly.

5. Now, peel off the skin of eggplants.

6. Place the eggplants, 2 teaspoons of oil and remaining ingredients except parsley and pulse until smooth.

7. Place the mixture into a serving bowl and refrigerate to chill before serving.

8. Drizzle with the remaining oil and serve with garnishing of fresh parsley.

Nutrition:

Calories: 75

Net Carbs: 4g

Carbohydrate: 9.3g

Fiber: 5.3g

Protein: 2.1g

Fat: 4.1g

Sugar: 4.2g

Sodium: 28mg

Salsa Verde

Servings: 10

Preparation time: 15 minutes

Cooking Time: 40 minutes

Ingredients

- 2 pounds medium tomatillos, husks removed and halved
- 2 large yellow onions, roughly chopped
- 6 garlic cloves, peeled and halved
- 2 Serrano peppers, seeded and chopped
- ¼ cup olive oil
- 1/3-½ cup water
- ½ cup fresh cilantro, chopped
- 2 tablespoons fresh lime juice
- Pinch of salt

Directions:

1. Preheat the oven to 425 degrees F.

2. In a large bowl, add the tomatillos, onions, garlic, peppers, and oil and toss to coat well.

3. Place the mixture onto 2 -15x10x1-inchbaking sheets and spread in an even layer.

4. Roast for about 35-40 minutes, stirring occasionally.

5. Remove both baking sheets from the oven and set aside to cool slightly.

6. Place the tomatillo mixture and enough water in a food processor and pulse until smooth.

7. Now, add the remaining ingredients and pulse until just combined.

8. Transfer the mixture into a bowl and refrigerate to chill before serving.

Nutrition:

Calories: 84

Net Carbs: 5.8g

Carbohydrate: 8.1g

Fiber: 2.3g

Protein: 1.3g

Fat: 6g

Sugar: 1g

Sodium: 18mg

Pizza Sauce

Servings: 8

Preparation time: 15 minutes

Cooking Time: 45 minutes

Ingredients

- 2 tablespoons olive oil
- 2 anchovy fillets
- 2 tablespoons fresh oregano leaves, finely chopped
- 3 garlic cloves, minced
- ½ teaspoon dried oregano, crushed
- ½ teaspoon red pepper flakes, crushed

- 1 -28-ouncescan whole peeled tomatoes, crushed
- ½ teaspoon Erythritol
- Salt, as required
- Pinch of freshly ground black pepper
- Pinch of organic baking powder

Directions:

1. Heat the olive oil in a medium pan over medium-low heat and cook the anchovy fillets for about 1 minute, stirring occasionally.

2. Stir in the fresh oregano, garlic, dried oregano, and red pepper flakes and sauté for about 2-3 minutes.

3. Add the remaining ingredients except baking powder and bring to a gentle simmer.

4. Reduce the heat to low and simmer for about 35-40 minutes, stirring occasionally.

5. Stir in the baking powder and remove from heat.

6. Set aside at room temperature to cool completely before serving.

7. You can preserve this sauce in refrigerator by placing into an airtight container.

Nutrition:

Calories: 56

Net Carbs: 3.4g

Carbohydrate: 5.1g

Fiber: 1.7g

Protein: 1.4g

Fat: 4g

Sugar: 2.7g

Sodium: 61mg

Marinara Sauce

Servings: 12

Preparation time: 10 minutes

Cooking Time: 5 minutes

Ingredients

- 2 tablespoons olive oil
- 1 garlic clove
- 2 teaspoons onion flakes
- 2 teaspoons fresh thyme, finely chopped
- 2 teaspoons fresh oregano, finely chopped
- 24 ounces tomato puree
- 1 tablespoon balsamic vinegar
- 2 teaspoons Erythritol
- Salt and ground black pepper, as required
- 2 tablespoons fresh parsley, finely chopped

Directions:

1. Heat the olive oil in a medium pan over medium-low heat and sauté the garlic, onion flakes, thyme and oregano for about 3 minutes.

2. Stir in the tomato puree, vinegar, Erythritol, salt, and black pepper and bring to a gentle simmer.

3. Remove the pan of sauce from heat and stir in the parsley.

4. Set aside at room temperature to cool completely before serving.

5. You can preserve this sauce in refrigerator by placing into an airtight container.

Nutrition:

Calories: 36

Net Carbs: 3.6g

Carbohydrate: 4.7g

Fiber: 1.1g

Protein: 0.9g

Fat: 2g

Sugar: 2.3g

Sodium: 168mg

BBQ Sauce

Servings: 20

Preparation time: 15 minutes

Cooking Time: 20 minutes

Ingredients

- 2½ -6-ouncescans tomato paste
- ½ cup organic apple cider vinegar
- 1/3 cup powdered Erythritol
- 2 tablespoons Worcestershire sauce
- 1 tablespoon liquid hickory smoke
- 2 teaspoons smoked paprika
- 1 teaspoon garlic powder
- ½ teaspoon onion powder
- Salt, as required
- ¼ teaspoon red chili powder
- ¼ teaspoon cayenne pepper
- 1½ cups water

Directions:

1. Add all the ingredients except water in a pan and beat until well combined.

2. Add 1 cup of water and beat until combined.

3. Add the remaining water and beat until well combined.

4. Place the pan over medium-high heat and bring to a gentle boil.

5. Adjust the heat to medium-low and simmer, uncovered for about 20 minutes, stirring frequently.

6. Remove from the heat and set aside to cool slightly before serving.

7. You can preserve this sauce in refrigerator by placing into an airtight container.

Nutrition:

Calories: 22

Net Carbs: 3.7g

Carbohydrate: 4.7g

Fiber: 1g

Protein: 1g

Fat: 0.1g

Sugar: 3g

Sodium: 85mg

Enchilada Sauce

Servings: 6

Preparation time: 10 minutes

Cooking Time: 10 minutes

Ingredients

- 3 ounces salted butter
- 1½ tablespoons Erythritol
- 2 teaspoons dried oregano
- 3 teaspoons ground cumin
- 2 teaspoons ground coriander

- 2 teaspoons onion powder
- ¼ teaspoon cayenne pepper
- Salt and ground black pepper, as required
- 12 ounces tomato puree

Directions:

1. Melt the butter in a medium pan over medium heat and sauté all the ingredients except tomato puree for about 3 minutes.

2. Add the tomato puree and simmer for about 5 minutes.

3. Remove the pan from heat and let it cool slightly before serving.

4. You can preserve this sauce in the refrigerator by placing into an airtight container.

Nutrition:

Calories: 132

Net Carbs: 5.1g

Carbohydrate: 6.6g

Fiber: 1.5g

Protein: 1.4g

Fat: 11.9g

Sugar: 3.1g

Sodium: 127mg

Note: You can add a little water, if you prefer a thinner sauce.

Teriyaki Sauce

Servings: 8

Preparation time: 10 minutes

Cooking Time: 15 minutes

Ingredients

- ½ cup low-sodium soy sauce
- 1 cup water
- 2 tablespoons organic apple cider vinegar
- ¼ cup Erythritol
- 1 tablespoon sesame oil
- ½ teaspoon ginger powder
- 2 teaspoons garlic powder
- ½ teaspoon xanthan gum
- 2 teaspoons sesame seeds

Directions:

1. Place all the ingredient except xanthan gum and sesame seeds in a small pan and mix well.

2. Now, place the pan over medium heat and bring to a boil.

3. Sprinkle with the xanthan gum and beat until well combined.

4. Cook for about 8-10 minutes or until the sauce becomes thick.

5. Remove the pan from heat and mix in the sesame seeds.

6. Serve hot.

7. You can preserve this cooled sauce in the refrigerator by placing into an airtight container.

Nutrition:

Calories: 29

Net Carbs: 1.6g

Carbohydrate: 2g

Fiber: 0.4g

Protein: 1.3g

Fat: 2.1g

Sugar: 1.2g

Sodium: 886mg

Hoisin Sauce

Servings: 8

Preparation time: 10 minutes

Cooking time: 0 minutes

Ingredients

- 4 tablespoons low-sodium soy sauce
- 2 tablespoons natural peanut butter
- 1 tablespoon Erythritol
- 2 teaspoons balsamic vinegar
- 2 teaspoons sesame oil
- 1 teaspoon Sriracha
- 1 garlic clove, peeled
- Ground black pepper, as required

Directions:

1. Add all the ingredients in a food processor and pulse until smooth.

2. You can preserve this sauce in the refrigerator by placing into an airtight container.

Nutrition:

Calories: 39

Net Carbs: 1.2g

Carbohydrate: 1.5g

Fiber: 0.3g

Protein: 1.8g

Fat: 3.1g

Sugar: 0.8g

Sodium: 445mg

Hot Sauce

Servings: 40

Preparation time: 15 minutes

Cooking Time: 15 minutes

Ingredients

- 1 tablespoon olive oil
- 1 cup carrot, peeled and chopped
- ½ cup yellow onion, chopped
- 5 garlic cloves, minced
- 6 habanero peppers, stemmed
- 1 tomato, chopped

- 1 tablespoon fresh lemon zest
- ¼ cup fresh lemon juice
- ¼ cup balsamic vinegar
- ¼ cup water
- Salt and ground black pepper, as required

Directions:

1. Heat the oil in a large pan over medium heat and cook the carrot, onion and garlic for about 8-10 minutes, stirring frequently.

2. Remove the pan from heat and let it cool slightly.

3. Place the onion mixture and remaining ingredients in a food processor and pulse until smooth.

4. Return the mixture into the same pan over medium-low heat and simmer for about 3-5 minutes, stirring occasionally.

5. Remove the pan from heat and let it cool completely.

6. You can preserve this sauce in the refrigerator by placing into an airtight container.

Nutrition:

Calories: 9

Net Carbs: 1g

Carbohydrate: 1.3g

Fiber: 0.3g

Protein: 0.2g

Fat: 0.4g

Sugar: 0.7g

Sodium: 7mg

Worcestershire Sauce

Servings: 10

Preparation time: 5 minutes

Cooking Time: 5 minutes

Ingredients

- ½ cup organic apple cider vinegar
- 2 tablespoons low-sodium soy sauce
- 2 tablespoons water
- ¼ teaspoon ground mustard
- ¼ teaspoon ground ginger
- ¼ teaspoon garlic powder
- ¼ teaspoon onion powder
- 1/8 teaspoon ground cinnamon
- 1/8 teaspoon ground black pepper

Directions:

1.   Add all the ingredients in a small pan and mix well.

2. Now, place the pan over medium heat and bring to a boil.

3. Adjust the heat to low and simmer for about 1-2 minutes.

4. Remove the pan from heat and let it cool completely.

5. You can preserve this sauce in refrigerator by placing into an airtight container.

Nutrition:

Calories: 5

Net Carbs: 0.4g

Carbohydrate: 0.5g

Fiber: 0.1g

Protein: 0.2g

Fat: 0g

Sugar: 0.3g

Sodium: 177mg

Almond Butter

Servings: 6

Preparation time: 15 minutes

Cooking Time: 15 minutes

Ingredients

- 2¼ cups raw almonds
- 1 tablespoon coconut oil
- ¾ teaspoon salt
- 4-6 drops liquid stevia
- ½ teaspoon ground cinnamon

Directions:

1.   Preheat the oven to 325 degrees F.

2. Arrange the almonds onto a rimmed baking sheet in an even layer.

3. Bake for about 12-15 minutes.

4. Remove the almonds from oven and let them cool completely.

5. In a food processor, fitted with metal blade, place the almonds and pulse until a fine meal forms.

6. Add the coconut oil, and salt and pulse for about 6-9 minutes.

7. Add the stevia, and cinnamon and pulse for about 1-2 minutes.

8. You can preserve this almond butter in refrigerator by placing into an airtight container.

Nutrition:

Calories: 226

Net Carbs: 3.2g

Carbohydrate: 7.8g

Fiber: 4.6g

Protein: 7.6g

Fat: 20.1g

Sugar: 1.5g

Sodium: 291mg

Mayonnaise

Servings: 10

Preparation time: 10 minutes

Cooking time: 0 minutes

Ingredients

- 2 organic egg yolks
- 3 teaspoons fresh lemon juice, divided
- 1 teaspoon mustard
- ½ cup coconut oil, melted
- ½ cup olive oil
- Salt and ground black pepper, as required -optional

Directions:

1. Place the egg yolks, 1 teaspoon of lemon juice, and mustard in a blender and pulse until combined.

2. While the motor is running gradually, add both oils and pulse until a thick mixture forms.

3. Add the remaining lemon juice, salt, and black pepper and pulse until well combined.

4. You can preserve this mayonnaise in refrigerator by placing into an airtight container.

Nutrition:

Calories: 193

Net Carbs: 0.2g

Carbohydrate: 0.3g

Fiber: 0.1g

Protein: 0.6g

Fat: 22g

Sugar: 0.1g

Sodium: 17mg

Note: If the mayonnaise seems too thin, slowly add more oils while the motor is running until thick.

Seasoned Salt

Servings: 18

Preparation time: 5 minutes

Cooking time: 0 minutes

Ingredients

- ¼ cup kosher salt
- ½ teaspoon onion powder
- 1 teaspoon garlic powder
- 1 teaspoon paprika
- ½ teaspoon ground red pepper
- 4 teaspoons freshly ground black pepper

Directions:

- Add all the ingredients in a bowl and stir to combine.
- Transfer into an airtight jar to preserve.

Nutrition:

Calories: 2

Net Carbs: 0.4g

Carbohydrate: 0.6g

Fiber: 0.2g

Protein: 0.1g

Fat: 0.1g

Sugar: 0.1g

Sodium: 1500mg

Poultry Seasoning

Servings: 10

Preparation time: 5 minutes

Cooking time: 0 minutes

Ingredients

- 2 teaspoons dried sage, crushed finely

- 1 teaspoon dried marjoram, crushed finely
- ¾ teaspoon dried rosemary, crushed finely
- 1½ teaspoons dried thyme, crushed finely
- ½ teaspoon ground nutmeg
- ½ teaspoon ground black pepper

Directions:

1. Add all the ingredients in a bowl and stir to combine.

2. Transfer into an airtight jar to preserve.

Nutrition:

Calories: 2

Net Carbs: 0.2g

Carbohydrate: 0.4g

Fiber: 0.2g

Protein: 0.1g

Fat: 0.1g

Sugar: 0g

Sodium: 0mg

Taco Seasoning

Servings: 12

Preparation time: 5 minutes

Cooking time: 0 minutes

Ingredients

- ½ teaspoon dried oregano, crushed
- ½ teaspoon ground cumin
- 2 teaspoons hot chili powder
- 1½ teaspoons paprika
- Pinch of red pepper flakes, crushed
- Pinch of cayenne pepper
- ¼ teaspoon ground black pepper
- 1 teaspoon onion powder
- ½ teaspoon garlic powder
- ½ teaspoon sea salt

Directions:

1.   Add all the ingredients in a bowl and stir to combine.

2. Transfer into an airtight jar to preserve.

Nutrition:

Calories: 4

Net Carbs: 0.5g

Carbohydrate: 0.8g

Fiber: 0.3g

Protein: 0.2g

Fat: 0.1g

Sugar: 0.2g

Sodium: 83mg

Pumpkin Pie Spice

Servings: 3

Preparation time: 5 minutes

Ingredients

- 1 teaspoon ground cinnamon
- ¼ teaspoon ground ginger
- ¼ teaspoon ground nutmeg
- 1/8 teaspoon ground cloves

Directions:

1. Add all the ingredients in a bowl and stir to combine.

2. Transfer into an airtight jar to preserve.

Nutrition:

Calories: 4

Net Carbs: 0.4g

Carbohydrate: 0.9g

Fiber: 0.5g

Protein: 0.1g

Fat: 0.1g

Sugar: 0.1g

Sodium: 0mg

Curry Powder

Servings: 20

Preparation time: 10 minutes

Cooking Time: 10 minutes

Ingredients

- ¼ cup coriander seeds
- 2 tablespoons mustard seeds
- 2 tablespoons cumin seeds
- 2 tablespoons anise seeds
- 1 tablespoon whole allspice berries

- 1 tablespoon fenugreek seeds
- 5 tablespoons ground turmeric

Directions:

1. In a large nonstick frying pan, place all the spices except turmeric over medium heat and cook for about 9-10 minutes or until toasted completely, stirring continuously.

2. Remove the frying pan from heat and set aside to cool.

3. In a spice grinder, add the toasted spices, and turmeric and grind until a fine powder forms.

4. Transfer into an airtight jar to preserve.

Nutrition:

Calories: 19

Net Carbs: 0.6g

Carbohydrate: 2.4g

Fiber: 1.8g

Protein: 0.8g

Fat: 0.8g

Sugar: 0.1g

Sodium: 2mg

Snacks

Chickpeas and Pepper Hummus

Preparation time: 10 minutes

Cooking time: 0 minutes

Servings: 4

Ingredients:

- 14 ounces canned chickpeas, no-salt-added, drained and rinsed
- 1 tablespoon sesame paste

- 2 roasted red peppers, chopped
- Juice of ½ lemon
- 4 walnuts, chopped

Directions:

1.   In your blender, combine the chickpeas with the sesame paste, red peppers, lemon juice and walnuts, pulse well, divide into bowls and serve as a snack.

2. Enjoy!

Nutrition: calories 231, fat 12, fiber 6, carbs 15, protein 14

Lemony Chickpeas Dip

Preparation time: 10 minutes

Cooking time: 0 minutes

Servings: 4

Ingredients:

- 14 ounces canned chickpeas, drained, no-salt-added, rinsed
- Zest of 1 lemon, grated
- Juice of 1 lemon
- 1 tablespoon olive oil
- 4 tablespoons pine nuts
- ½ cup coriander, chopped

Directions:

1. In a blender, combine the chickpeas with lemon zest, lemon juice, coriander and oil, pulse well, divide into small bowls, sprinkle pine nuts on top and serve as a party dip.

2. Enjoy!

Nutrition: calories 200, fat 12, fiber 4, carbs 9, protein 7

Chili Nuts

Preparation time: 10 minutes

Cooking time: 10 minutes

Servings: 4

Ingredients:

- ½ teaspoon chili flakes
- 1 egg white
- ½ teaspoon curry powder
- ½ teaspoon ginger powder
- 4 tablespoons coconut sugar
- A pinch of cayenne pepper
- 14 ounces mixed nuts

Directions:

1. In a bowl, combine the egg white with the chili flakes, curry powder, curry powder, ginger powder, coconut sugar and cayenne and whisk well.

2. Add the nuts, toss well, spread them on a lined baking sheet, introduce in the oven and bake at 400 degrees F for 10 minutes.

3. Divide the nuts into bowls and serve as a snack.

4. Enjoy!

Nutrition: calories 234, fat 12, fiber 5, carbs 14, protein 7

Protein Bars

Preparation time: 10 minutes

Cooking time: 0 minutes

Servings: 4

Ingredients:

- 4 ounces apricots, dried
- 2 ounces water
- 2 tablespoons rolled oats
- 1 tablespoon sunflower seeds
- 2 tablespoons coconut, shredded
- 1 tablespoon sesame seeds
- 1 tablespoon cranberries

- 3 tablespoons hemp seeds
- 1 tablespoon chia seeds

Directions:

1. In your food processor, combine the apricots with the water and the oats, pulse well, transfer to a bowl, add coconut, sunflower seeds, sesame seeds, cranberries, hemp and chia seeds and stir until you obtain a paste.

2. Roll this into a log, wrap, cool in the fridge, slice and serve as a snack.

3. Enjoy!

Nutrition: calories 100, fat 3, fiber 4, carbs 8, protein 5

Red Pepper Muffins

Preparation time: 10 minutes

Cooking time: 30 minutes

Servings: 12

Ingredients:

- 1 and ¾ cups whole wheat flour
- 2 teaspoons baking powder
- 2 tablespoons coconut sugar
- A pinch of black pepper
- 1 egg
- ¾ cup almond milk
- 2/3 cup roasted red pepper, chopped

- ½ cup low-fat mozzarella, shredded

Directions:

1. In a bowl, combine the flour with baking powder, coconut sugar, black pepper, egg, milk, red pepper and mozzarella, stir well, divide into a lined muffin tray, introduce in the oven and bake at 400 degrees F for 30 minutes.

2. Serve as a snack.

3. Enjoy!

Nutrition: calories 149, fat 4, fiber 2, carbs 14, protein 5

Nuts and Seeds Mix

Preparation time: 10 minutes

Cooking time: 0 minutes

Servings: 6

Ingredients:

- 1 cup pecans
- 1 cup hazelnuts
- 1 cup almonds
- ¼ cup coconut, shredded
- 1 cup walnuts
- ½ cup papaya pieces, dried
- ½ cup dates, dried, pitted and chopped
- ½ cup sunflower seeds
- ½ cup pumpkin seeds
- 1 cup raisins

Directions:

1. In a bowl, combine the pecans with the hazelnuts, almonds, coconut, walnuts, papaya,

dates, sunflower seeds, pumpkin seeds and raisins, toss and serve as a snack.

2. Enjoy!

Nutrition: calories 188, fat 4, fiber 6, carbs 8, protein 6

Kale Chips

Preparation time: 10 minutes

Cooking time: 15 minutes

Servings: 8

Ingredients:

- 1 bunch kale leaves
- 1 tablespoon olive oil
- 1 teaspoon smoked paprika
- A pinch of black pepper

Directions:

1. Spread the kale leaves on a baking sheet, add black pepper, oil and paprika, toss, introduce in the oven and bake at 350 degrees F for 15 minutes.

2. Divide into bowls and serve as a snack.

3. Enjoy!

Nutrition: calories 177, fat 2, fiber 4, carbs 13, protein 6

Potato Chips

Preparation time: 10 minutes

Cooking time: 30 minutes

Servings: 6

Ingredients:

- 2 gold potatoes, cut into thin rounds
- 1 tablespoon olive oil
- 2 teaspoons garlic, minced

Directions:

1. In a bowl, combine the potato chips with the oil and the garlic, toss, spread on a lined baking sheet, introduce in the oven and bake at 400 degrees F for 30 minutes.

2. Divide into bowls and serve.

3. Enjoy!

Nutrition: calories 200, fat 3, fiber 5, carbs 13, protein 6

Peach Dip

Preparation time: 10 minutes

Cooking time: 0 minutes

Servings: 2

Ingredients:

- ½ cup nonfat yogurt
- 1 cup peaches, chopped
- A pinch of cinnamon powder
- A pinch of nutmeg, ground

Directions:

1. In a bowl, combine the yogurt with the peaches, cinnamon and nutmeg, whisk, divide into small bowls and serve as a snack.

2. Enjoy!

Nutrition: calories 165, fat 2, fiber 3, carbs 14, protein 13

Cereal Mix

Preparation time: 10 minutes

Cooking time: 40 minutes

Servings: 6

Ingredients:

- 3 tablespoons olive oil
- 1 teaspoon hot sauce
- ½ teaspoon garlic powder
- ½ teaspoon onion powder
- ½ teaspoon cumin, ground
- A pinch of cayenne pepper
- 3 cups rice cereal squares
- 1 cup cornflakes
- ½ cup pepitas

Directions:

1. In a bowl, combine the oil with the hot sauce, garlic powder, onion powder, cumin, cayenne, rice cereal, cornflakes and pepitas, toss, spread on a lined baking sheet, introduce in the oven and bake at 350 degrees F for 40 minutes.

2. Divide into bowls and serve as a snack.

3. Enjoy!

Nutrition: calories 199, fat 3, fiber 4, carbs 12, protein 5

Goji Berry Mix

Preparation time: 10 minutes

Cooking time: 0 minutes

Servings: 4

Ingredients:

- 1 cup almonds
- 1 cup goji berries
- ½ cup sunflower seeds
- ½ cup pumpkin seeds
- ½ cup walnuts, halved
- 12 apricots, dried and quartered

Directions:

1. In a bowl, combine the almond with the goji berries, sunflower seeds, pumpkin seeds, walnuts and apricots, toss, divide into bowls and serve.

2. Enjoy!

Nutrition: calories 187, fat 2, fiber 5, carbs 12, protein 6

Artichoke Spread

Preparation time: 10 minutes

Cooking time: 15 minutes

Servings: 4

Ingredients:

- 10 ounces spinach, chopped
- 12 ounces canned artichoke hearts, no-salt-added, drained and chopped
- 1 cup coconut cream
- 1 cup low-fat cheddar, shredded
- A pinch of black pepper

Directions:

1. In a bowl, combine the spinach with the artichokes, cream, cheese and black pepper, stir well, transfer to a baking dish, introduce in the oven and bake at 400 degrees F for 15 minutes.

2. Divide into bowls and serve.

3. Enjoy!

Nutrition: calories 200, fat 4, fiber 6, carbs 14, protein 8

Avocado Salsa

Preparation time: 10 minutes

Cooking time: 0 minutes

Servings: 4

Ingredients:

- 1 small yellow onion, minced

- 1 jalapeno, minced
- ¼ cup cilantro, chopped
- A pinch of black pepper
- 2 avocados, peeled, pitted and cubed
- 2 tablespoons lime juice

Directions:

1.	In a bowl, combine the onion with the jalapeno, cilantro, black pepper, avocado and lime juice, toss and serve.

2. Enjoy!

Nutrition: calories 198, fat 2, fiber 5, carbs 14, protein 7

Onion Spread

Preparation time: 10 minutes

Cooking time: 35 minutes

Servings: 4

Ingredients:

- 2 tablespoons olive oil
- 2 yellow onions, sliced
- A pinch of black pepper
- 8 ounces low-fat cream cheese
- 1 cup coconut cream
- 2 tablespoons chives, chopped

Directions:

1. Heat up a pan with the oil over low heat, add the onions and the black pepper, stir and cook for 35 minutes.

2. In a bowl, combine the onions with the cream cheese, coconut cream and chives, stir well and serve as a party spread.

3. Enjoy!

Nutrition: calories 212, fat 3, fiber 5, carbs 14, protein 8

Eggplant Salsa

Preparation time: 10 minutes

Cooking time: 7 hours

Servings: 4

Ingredients:

- 1 and ½ cups tomatoes, chopped
- 3 cups eggplant, cubed
- 6 ounces green olives, pitted and sliced
- 4 garlic cloves, minced

- 2 teaspoons balsamic vinegar
- 1 tablespoon oregano, chopped
- Black pepper to the taste

Directions:

1. In your slow cooker, mix tomatoes with eggplant, green olives, garlic, vinegar, oregano and pepper, toss, cover, cook on Low for 7 hours, divide into small bowls and serve as an appetizer.

2. Enjoy!

Nutrition: calories 190, fat 6, fiber 5, carbs 12, protein 2

Artichoke and Beans Spread

Preparation time: 10 minutes

Cooking time: 30 minutes

Servings: 8

Ingredients:

- 4 cups spinach, chopped
- 2 cups artichoke hearts
- Black pepper to the taste
- 1 teaspoon thyme, chopped
- 2 garlic cloves, minced
- 1 cup white beans, already cooked
- 1 tablespoon parsley, chopped
- 2 tablespoons low-fat parmesan, grated
- ½ cup low-fat sour cream

Directions:

1. In your slow cooker, mix artichokes with spinach, black pepper, thyme, garlic, beans, parmesan, parsley and sour cream, stir, cover and cook on Low for 5 hours.

2. Transfer to your blender, pulse well divide into bowls and serve.

3. Enjoy!

Nutrition: calories 180, fat 2, fiber 6, carbs 11, protein 5

Stuffed White Mushrooms

Preparation time: 10 minutes

Cooking time: 5 hours

Servings: 20

Ingredients:

- 20 mushrooms, stems removed
- ¼ cup low-fat butter, melted
- 1 and ½ cups whole wheat breadcrumbs
- 2 tablespoons parsley, chopped
- 2 cups basil, chopped
- 1 cup tomato sauce, no-salt-added
- ¼ cup low-fat parmesan, grated
- 1 tablespoon garlic, minced
- 2 teaspoons lemon juice
- 1 tablespoon olive oil

Directions:

1. In a bowl, mix butter with breadcrumbs and parsley, stir well and leave aside.

2. In your blender, mix basil with oil, parmesan, garlic and lemon juice and pulse really well.

3. Stuff mushrooms with this mix, pour the tomato sauce on top, sprinkle breadcrumbs mix at the end, cover and cook on Low for 5 hours.

4. Arrange mushrooms on a platter and serve.

5. Enjoy!

Nutrition: calories 170, fat 1, fiber 3, carbs 14, protein 4

Italian Tomato Appetizer

Preparation time: 10 minutes

Cooking time: 2 hours

Servings: 4

Ingredients:

- 2 teaspoons olive oil
- 8 tomatoes, chopped
- ¼ cup basil, chopped

- 3 tablespoons low-sodium veggie stock
- 1 garlic clove, minced
- 4 Italian whole wheat bread slices, toasted
- Black pepper to the taste

Directions:

1. In your slow cooker, mix tomatoes with basil, garlic, oil, stock and black pepper, stir, cover, cook on High for 2 hours and then leave aside to cool down.

2. Divide this mix on the toasted bread and serve as an appetizer.

3. Enjoy!

Nutrition: calories 174, fat 2, fiber 1, carbs 10, protein 4

Sweet Pineapple Snack

Preparation time: 10 minutes

Cooking time: 2 hours

Servings: 8

Ingredients:

- 1 tablespoon lime juice
- 2 tablespoons stevia
- 1 tablespoon olive oil
- 1 teaspoon cinnamon powder
- 1 pineapple, peeled and cut into medium sticks
- ¼ teaspoon cloves, ground

- 1 tablespoon lime zest, grated

Directions:

1. In a bowl, mix lime juice with stevia, oil, cinnamon and cloves and whisk well.

2. Add the pineapple sticks to your slow cooker, add lime mix, toss, cover and cook on High for 2 hours.

3. Serve the pineapple sticks as a snack with lime zest sprinkled on top.

4. Enjoy!

Nutrition: calories 130, fat 4, fiber 1, carbs 10, protein 3

Chickpeas Hummus

Preparation time: 10 minutes

Cooking time: 5 hours

Servings: 6

Ingredients:

- 1 cup chickpeas, soaked overnight and drained
- 2 garlic cloves
- 3 cups water
- 1 tablespoon olive oil
- 2 tablespoons sherry vinegar
- ¾ cup green onions, chopped
- 1 teaspoon cumin, ground
- 3 tablespoons cilantro, chopped

Directions:

1. Put the water in your slow cooker, add chickpeas and garlic, cover and cook on Low for 5 hours.

2. Drain chickpeas, transfer them to your blender, add ½ cup of the cooking liquid, green onions, vinegar, oil, cilantro and cumin, blend well, divide into bowls and serve.

3. Enjoy!

Nutrition: calories 133, fat 1, fiber 3, carbs 10, protein 3

Asparagus Snack

Preparation time: 4 weeks

Cooking time: 2 hours

Servings: 6

Ingredients:

- 3 cups asparagus spears, halved
- ¼ cup apple cider vinegar
- 1 tablespoon dill
- ¼ cup white wine vinegar
- 2 cloves
- 1 cup water
- 3 garlic cloves, sliced
- ¼ teaspoon red pepper flakes
- 8 black peppercorns
- 1 teaspoon coriander seeds

Directions:

1. In your slow cooker, mix the asparagus with the cider vinegar, white vinegar, dill, cloves, water, garlic, pepper flakes, peppercorns and coriander, cover and cook on High for 2 hours.

2. Drain asparagus, transfer it to bowls and serve as a snack.

3. Enjoy!

Nutrition: calories 90, fat 1, fiber 2, carbs 7, protein 2

Shrimp and Beans Appetizer Salad

Preparation time: 10 minutes

Cooking time: 5 hours and 30 minutes.

Servings: 8

Ingredients:

- ¼ pound shrimp, peeled, deveined and chopped
- Zest and juice of 2 limes
- Zest and juice of 2 lemons
- 2 teaspoons cumin, ground
- 2 tablespoons olive oil
- 1 cup tomato, chopped
- ½ cup red onion, chopped
- 2 tablespoons garlic, minced
- 1 cup canned black beans, no-salt-added, drained and rinsed
- 1 cup cucumber, chopped
- ¼ cup cilantro, chopped

Directions:

1. In a bowl, mix lime juice and lemon juice with shrimp and toss.

2. Grease the slow cooker with the oil, add black beans, tomato, onion, garlic and cumin, cover and cook on Low for 5 hours.

3. Add shrimp, cover, cook on Low for 30 minutes, more, transfer everything to a bowl, add cucumber and cilantro,

toss, leave aside to cool down, divide between small bowls and serve as an appetizer.

4. Enjoy!

Nutrition: calories 200, fat 3, fiber 2, carbs 15, protein 5

Pepper and Chickpeas Dip

Preparation time: 10 minutes

Cooking time: 2 hours

Servings: 12

Ingredients:

- 1 cup red bell pepper, sliced
- 1 tablespoon olive oil
- 2 tablespoons white sesame seeds
- 2 cups canned chickpeas, no-salt-added, drained and rinsed
- 1 tablespoon lemon juice
- 1 teaspoon garlic powder
- 1 teaspoon onion powder
- A pinch of cayenne pepper
- 1 and ¼ teaspoons cumin, ground

Directions:

1. In your slow cooker, mix red bell pepper with oil, sesame seeds, chickpeas, lemon juice, garlic and onion powder, cayenne pepper and cumin, cover and cook on High for 2 hours.

2. Transfer this mix to your blender, pulse well, divide into serving bowls and serve cold.

3. Enjoy!

Nutrition: calories 180, fat 2, fiber 2, carbs 15, protein 3

White Bean Spread

Preparation time: 10 minutes

Cooking time: 6 hours

Servings: 8

Ingredients:

- 15 ounces canned white beans, no-salt-added, drained and rinsed
- 1 cup low-sodium veggie stock

- 2 tablespoons olive oil

- 8 garlic cloves, roasted

- 2 tablespoons lemon juice

Directions:

1.   In your blender, mix beans with oil, stock, garlic and lemon juice, cover, cook on Low for 6 hours, transfer to your blender, pulse well, divide into bowls and serve as a snack.

2. Enjoy!

Nutrition: calories 159, fat 4, fiber 3, carbs 14, protein 2

Minty Spinach Dip

Preparation time: 20 minutes

Cooking time: 2 hours

Servings: 4

Ingredients:

- 1 bunch spinach leaves, roughly chopped
- 1 scallion, sliced
- 2 tablespoons mint leaves, chopped
- ¾ cup low-fat sour cream
- Black pepper to the taste

Directions:

1. In your slow cooker, mix the spinach with the scallion, mint, cream and black pepper, cover, and cook on High for 2 hours, stir well, divide into bowls and serve.

2. Enjoy!

Nutrition: calories 160, fat 3, fiber 3, carbs 12, protein 5

Turnips and Cauliflower Spread

Preparation time: 10 minutes

Cooking time: 7 hours

Servings: 4

Ingredients:

- 2 cups cauliflower florets
- 1/3 cup cashews, chopped
- 1 cup turnips, chopped
- 2 and ½ cups water
- 1 cup coconut milk
- 1 teaspoon garlic powder
- ¼ teaspoon smoked paprika
- ¼ teaspoon mustard powder

Directions:

1. In your slow cooker, mix cauliflower with cashews, turnips and water, stir, cover, cook on Low for 7 hours, drain, transfer to a blender, add milk, garlic powder, paprika and mustard powder, blend well, divide into bowls and serve as a snack

2. Enjoy!

Nutrition: calories 221, fat 7, fiber 4, carbs 14, protein 3g